igloo

First published in 2007 by Igloo Books Ltd
Cottage Farm, Sywell,
Northants, NN6 0BJ
www.igloo-books.com

Copyright © 2007 Igloo Books Ltd

ISBN: 978-1-84561-630-4

Illustrations by Martin Impey

Printed in China

My Book of Firsts

My name is ....

I was born on ....

My first home

We lived here for …… years

My favourite room in the house
was ……………………………

photo

Address………………………
………………………………
………………………………
………………………………

My first bedroom

The colour of my bedroom was

....

The first picture on my wall was

....

My first favourite things

My first favourite TV show

....

My first favourite character

....

My first favourite toy ....

My first favourite food

....

....

My first favourite book ....

My first best friend ....

A photo of me and
my best friend

My first favourite outfit ....

The first time I...

years old.

... did a roly poly I was ....

.....caught my first ball when I was ...... years old.

I was playing with ....

.....rode a bike when I was .... years old

The colour of the bike was ....

... went swimming I was ...... years old.

My first holiday

We went to ....

We went for .... days, on (date)

....

I went with ....

....

We got there by ....

We stayed in a ....

The weather was ....

My first
holiday
photos

My firsts

My first tooth came through when I was ………. years old.

My first trip to the dentist was

when I was …… years old.

I went with …………………

My first haircut was when I was …….. years old.

The first time I danced was with ....

My first pet was a ....

called ....

My first pair of shoes were the colour ....

The first time I...

...said a nursery rhyme I was ...... years old.

The rhyme was ......

....

....

....

...sang a song I was ...... years old.

The song was called ....

...said my ABCs, I was ......years old.

...wrote my name I was ...... years old.

...said my numbers from 1 to 10, I was

1 2 3 4 5 6 7 8 9 10

.... years old.

...knew my colours, I was ...... years old.

My world

My first trip to the park was
when I was ..... years old.

I went on the

....

....

....

....

....

My first picnic was with

....

....

We ate ....

....

....

My first trip to the beach was when I was . . . . . . years old.

We went to . . . .

. . . .

My first trip to the cinema was to see . . . .

My first meal in a restaurant was with . . . .

. . . .

. . . .

. . . .

The restaurant was called

. . . .

The first time I...

. . . fed myself I was . . . . . . years old.

. . . slept in a big bed
I was . . . . . . years old.

. . . dressed myself I wore

. . . .

. . . .

. . . .

I was . . . . . . years old.

.....drew a picture it was of a ....when I was .... years old.

My first journeys

My first car ride was with

....

....

when I was ......years old.

My first bus trip was with

....

....

when I was ......years old.

My first train trip was

from ....

....

to ....

....

My first plane trip was to ....

My first boat trip was when I was .... years old.

My first day...

... at nursery was on

....

The school was called

....

....

My favourite teacher's
name was

....

. . . at school was on . . . .

The colour of my uniform was . . . .

The name of my school was . . . .

My favourite lesson was

My first Christmas

My first Christmas morning was at ....

My first Christmas present was ....

For my first Christmas Day dinner I ate ....
....

I spent my first Christmas with ....
....

My first Birthday

My first birthday
present was

. . . .

. . . .

My birthday guests
were . . . .

. . . .

. . . .

. . . .

I was . . . . tall

My first cake was made of . . . .

My second Birthday

My birthday cake was made of . . . .

My favourite

present was

. . . .

What I did

. . . .

. . . .

I was . . . . tall

My third Birthday

My birthday cake was made of . . . .

My favourite present was . . . .

What I did . . . .

I was . . . . tall

My fourth Birthday

My birthday cake was made of . . . .

My favourite
present was

. . . .

What I did

. . . .

. . . .

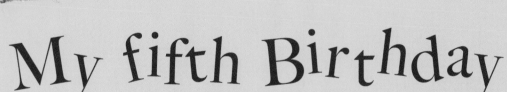

I was . . . . tall

My fifth Birthday

My birthday cake was made of . . . .

My favourite present was . . . .

What I did . . . .

I was . . . . tall